Peter Dixon Books

Creative Expression *(Blackwells)*

Early Years *(Mitchell-Beazley)*

Grow Your Own Poems *(Thomas Nelson)*

I Heard a Spider Sobbing *(Peche Luna)*

BIG BILLY

Peter Dixon

ILLUSTRATED BY DAVID THOMAS

1990

First published 1990
Second impression 1991
Third impression 1993
Fourth impression 1996
Fifth impression 1997

Printed by Sarsen Press
22 Hyde Street, Winchester

ISBN 1 873195 01 X

Further copies are available from
Peche Luna
30 Cheriton Road
Winchester England
SO22 5AX

This book is for everyone, anyone, and jellyone.
It is for big people, small people, in between people.
Hoppers and jumpers the world over.
It is for bird watchers, telly watchers, and people who like
hanging around doing nothing much.

It is for losing, finding, reading on late trains and leaving on blue
buses.
It is for people who are five years old, ninety years old, good
spellers, bad spellers, good readers and bad readers.
It is for candyfloss crunchers and puddle jumpers.
It is for bikers, hikers and red kite likers.

It isn't for infants and it isn't for juniors, seniors, Chelsea
Pensioners or Sheffield Wednesday Pensioners...
because it is for everyone...
But most of all for people just like you.

POEMS

Good news! Since writing this poem I have been back to the lake and it is still just about alive. Keep your fingers crossed.

I was always a shepherd. Why not invent your own play and then you could write yourself the part you've always really wanted.

I enjoy piers yet so many seem to disappear. Are there any very ancient buildings down your way that deserve a poem or two?

Phew! Take a big breath and see if you can be as good as Jeff. I was not going to include this poem, but at least it is a bit different. Can you write a different kind of poem?

I wrote this laying on the beach. Holiday time is a good time for poetry writing because you need tons of time with nothing else troubling you.

I really do like flies. I just wish they were not so dirty then everyone would like them.

I hope you help all spiders out of the bath and don't wash them down the plug hole. They are very clever creatures and excellent for writing poems about. Well, I think so. So please don't kill them, or there won't be any left to write about.

Sometimes you can make pictures mix easily with words. I don't know where I got this idea from, it just came. Don't plan your poems out too carefully, just start them off and let them take you along. Sometimes they don't lead you anywhere much, but upon other occasions they take you to wonderful new places.

I bet we've all seen a dead cat - somewhere. I wonder how many people stopped and wrote a poem about it. Whenever you come across something 'different' then have a think and say to yourself: 'Could I do a poem about this ...?'

Poems can be very short. There is nothing good about poems that are long. The important thing is that they say what they want to say. Long or short, it does not matter.

The last line sort of 'came' all by itself. I did not set out to write the poem this way, it just happened. Poems are alive as you write them, they often find their own words and ways.

Simple and true. Diggers find so much.

How about another poem called 'Assembly' or 'Dinnertime'.

When Norma asked her son where he wanted to go for his holiday he said 'Boglins'. Where do you think he meant?

I am sure everyone could add a few extra lines to this.

What do you think about in bed, just before you doze off? Dreams are interesting but I still think real events and real memories make the best poems. Take a pencil and paper to bed. Tonight.

BIG BILLY

There's a spider in the bathroom
With legs as thick as rope.
It lives behind the cupboard
Where my mother keeps the soap.
My sister calls it Billy,
She says he creeps each night
Into children's bedrooms
(when they turn out the light).

I lay and hear him coming.
I hear his spider breath,
Huffing up the passage
With gasps as dark as death.
I hide beneath my duvet
... but the sides they won't tuck in ...
And I know he'll find a pathway
And I know that Billy'll win!

I know he's going to get me.
I know he's going to come
And he's going to eat my sister
And he's going to get my Mum ...
He's going to eat the family,
He's going to eat us all
'Cos Billy's really awful ...

         ...and he's coming up the hall !!!

PLEASE SIR!!

There's a fight .... Sir!
In the cloakroom .... Sir!
And Arnie's strangled Paul,
Smithy's strangled Watson
'cos Watson took his ball.
Barny's ripped his shirt .... Sir!
And Baker spat on Sue,
She was only tryin' to stop them
And she's got it on her shoe.
The helper lady went .... Sir!
She said she couldn't stay,
Jane's crying in the toilets
And the gerbil's got away ...

Garnett knocked the cage........ Sir!
The door, it just flipped back,
And it ran behind the cupboard
And it's stuck inside a crack.

We poked it with a stick .... Sir!
But the powder paint got spilt,
It's over all the carpet
And it's over Helen's kilt.

I think you ought to come........ Sir!
Mildred Miles was sick
And all the boys are yellin'
And Martin threw a brick.
It nearly hit John Bentley
And he's going to tell his Mum,
So shall I say you're comin'
And shall I fetch his Mum?

Shall we get the cleaners?
And can I mop the paint?
The new boy's torn his jacket
And he thinks he's going to faint .
The other teachers said .... Sir!
That I should come to you
'Cos you're the Duty Teacher
So you'll know what to do
.... Sir!

BUGSY

Bugsy in the pet shop
ran away
Bugsy
Bugsy
out to play.
Rabbit in the cornfield
one
two
three.
Bugsy
Bugsy
running free.
Rabbit in the woodland
eight
nine
ten
Five are ladies
five are men.
A hundred in the garden
running on the lawn
a thousand in the burrow
just being born.
A million in the meadow
a billion on the way ...
    Bugsy
    Bugsy
        Happy Day.

CONVERSATION WITH MR. LANE THE DENTIST

Open wide, lets take a look
Is everything O.K.?

'Gwargollygog - gwargollygog
gwargollygog - glubglay.'

A spot just here, amalgam please
rinse then spit again
tell me if I'm hurting
say if you feel pain.

'Gwargollygog - gwargollygog
gwargollygog - glubglay.'

Now just a little drilling
now just a little more
would you like a rinse out
or shall I do some more?

'Gwargollygog - gwargollygog
gwargollygog - glubglay.'

Now you can open wider
lets have another look
and did you bring the blue form
and did you sign the book?

'Gwargollygog - gwargollygog
gwargollygog - glubglay.'

Now push your tongue right over
and have you been away
did you have good weather
where was your holiday?

'Gwargollygog - gwargollygog
gwargollygog - glubglay...'

Gwargollygog - gwargollygog
that sounds awfully nice
is it hot and sunny
or is it snow and ice?

This molars just erupting
the filling's in a mess

and who is it you stay with
and have you their address?

'Gwargollygog - gwargollygog
gwargollygog - glubglay.'

Was the hotel comfy
and are the beaches clean
was the airport busy
- where was it that you'd been?

'Gwargollygog - gwargollygog
gwargollygog - glubglay...'

Ah - yes that's right you told me
a lovely little place
try to keep your head still
and please don't twist your face.
I've very nearly finished
but you'll feel a little numb
did you go with schoolfriends
- or with your dad and mum?

'Gwargollygog - gwargollygog
gwargollygog - glubglay...'

Gwargollygwog - gwargollygwog
gwargollygog - you say
I really do not know them
foreign friends
- are they?

They sound such lovely people
good friends are always fun
now only chew on one side
and do not chew on gum.
Come and see me next week

we'll have another look
good afternoon Miss Smedley

Gwargollygog
Gubglook!

ON THE FARM

My name is Mr. Brown Nose
and I live on Cuckoo Farm,
I live with lots of ladies
- who I really love to charm.

They love the gold ring in my nose
they love my droopy eyes,
- but I've got dreadful problems
for I've got AWFUL flies!

Pheeeeeeeeeeeeeeewww ...

They're really really shocking
they're really really bad,
they itch me stupid crazy
they itch me snorting mad.

They get right up my whiskers
they wriggle up my nose,
and dance upon my knee caps
and tickle on my toes.

The tractor does not get them
the cat gets just a few
- I saw one on a chicken
and on the farmer's shoe.

I saw one on the turkey's beak
I saw one on it's tail,
I saw one on a pitchfork
and another on a pail ...

I never mind the ones and twos
even threes - or fours,
but I get tons of millions
zillions zillions more.

The hens and geese don't seem to care
The pigs just stand and smile,
they never bother balers
combines
    paths
      or stiles.

But they drive me really silly.
I stamp around and roar,
Then others hear me bellow
and buzzzzz in through my door.

"LOOK THERE HE IS ... " calls Betty Fly

"Yes, there he is ... " they shout

then they tickle up my bottom
and they tickle up my snout.
My life is really rotten
and I don't know what to do ...

      I think the only answer
      is to send them round ...

           to you.

MY MUM

My Mum was a mince pie of a mum.
A 'doyouwantabiscuitwithyourtea?'
kind of mum.
A roast potato
    brown gravy
    crackle on the pork
    yorkshire pud
kind of lady.
She was a
    houseful of everyone
    polish the brass
    whiten the step
    rush to the shops
    bucket and mops
kind of lady.

A -   'hello dear'
        always near
        hurry scurry
'Oh, don't worry ...'
kind of Mum.

She collected -
    old people
    funny stories
    and other people's children.

She called everyone by an invented name
and was a champion
                bus waiter
                queuer
                visitor
                laugher
        and Nutall Mint sucker.

She was someone
who
would give anyone
her last mint.

TADPOLES

Said the tadpole to the tadpole
as they tadpoled round their jar
I don't want to be a froggy
I don't want to grow that far.
I'm happy as I am now
black blob and little tail,
I don't want to be a froggy
or a toady
or a whale.

I just want to be a taddy
I want to stay the same,
I liked being frogspawn
I didn't want to change ...
Oh, why've I got to grow up
and be an ugly toad,
creep around in ditches
— and get squashed in the road.
I'd like to stay a taddy
stay the same for life.
This jar can be my palace ...

and you can be my wife.

WALLABIES

Do wallabies have holidays
- hop off to other spots?
Tag along with tigers
and sail the seas on yachts?

Do they ski on icy mountains
in trousers painted pink?
Ride upon a ski-lift
and skate upon a rink?

Do they cruise to cultured places
tour the Holy Land?
See alot of statues
and see a lot of sand?

Do they strut around the Boulevards
Do they gobble Frenchmen's snails?
Visit bonny Bombay
see fakirs sit on nails?

Do they like a plate of curry
- a Chinese take away?
Dancing at a disco
in a Corfu sort of way?

Do they like to ride on horses
do they pot hole,
            fish
            or climb?
Wander round a gallery
and have an arty time?

I wonder where they're going
as I watch them hopping past

— it must be somewhere special
'cos they go so very fast!

SCHOOL TRIP

I saw a man in a cardboard box
I saw a lady too,
Her head was wrapped in paper,
She only had one shoe.
We went and saw where Nelson is
We visited St. Pauls,
We visited the Palace
and we climbed the city walls.

We saw the Tower Bridge open,
We went and saw Big Ben

...but I remember ladies
and boxes full of men.

A POEM OF BOXER'S LAKE

Boxer's lake is dying
(does Mr. Boxer know?)
The place I caught my carpfish
Two score years ago.

> My world of grass and rushes
> My world of bread and paste
> setting sun in ripples,
> running home - too late.
> Yes,
> Boxer's Lake is dying
> tombstone floating fish,
> white as water lily
> white as morning mist ...

> White as bankside parsley
> bloated bulging eyes,
> jogging in the rushes
> jogging with the flies.

Yes,
Boxer's Lake is dying
another world is dead,
it didn't make a profit
so a price was on it's head.

NATIVITY PLAY

This year ...
This year can I be Herod?
This year, can I be him?
A wiseman
or a Joseph?
An inn man
or a king?

This year ...
can I be famous?
This year, can I be best?
Bear a crown of silver
and wear a golden vest?

This year ...
can I be starlight?
This year, can I stand out?

... feel the swish of curtains
and hear the front row shout
'Hurrah' for good old Ronny
he brings a gift of gold
head afire with tinsel
'The Greatest Story Told...'
'Hurrah for good old Herod!'
and shepherds from afar.

So -
don't make me a palm tree
And can I be -
                    a Star.

TOO COSTLY TO MAINTAIN

Today _
At mid-day
They blew up the pier ...
 and ten thousand memories,
  smiles
   and foolish family photos.

No more tangled fishing lines
  dropped shillings
  and lovers kisses,
For today they blew up the pier.

A man from Birmingham did it
With a button -
  and faded bunting.

I saw no flash,
Flying debris
Or wave of cheerful T.V. crew ...

  Just the ghost of steamers
  Polka dressed girls
  The song of trippers

  and the cry of the boatmen.

JEFFTHEBREATH

Jeff
(The Breath)
was the Welsh
Holdyourbreathforaslongasyoucan
Champion
1970
   71
   72
   73
   75
   75
   76
   77
   78
   79
   80
   81
   82
   83
   84 ...5
        six, seven, eight, nine,
and ten.

Jeff
(The Breath)
couldholdhisbreathlonger
thananyoneelseinthevalley

until

he met Sung
the Cardiff Take-away man
in breath-taking combat
at Llygwellygrellybrwellpantogy
on
a keepWalesfortheWelshmountainside

where
Sung (The Lung)
Wung
by an age.

32

Sung is now reigning
in peace

but Jeffthebreath
lives to gasp

onanotherdayonaWelshmountainside

33

CORFU '88

There they lie
Flattened
Red as pedallos
And greasy as last night's Taverna chips.
Blackeyed
Pebblepocked
And limp.

'We'll pay for this'
Announces the vermillioned accountant
                            from Kent.
'We'll pay for this ....'

But the noisy French drown his warning
And the girl from page three
Scowls
Smooths her honied flesh
And reaches out

To turn up the sun.

A HAPPY TAIL

No-one much liked Bertie fly.
No, no-one seemed to care,
they smacked him on the ceiling
and they smacked him on the chair.

They smote him on the babyfood
they smote him on the bread,
they smote him at the butchers
and they smote him on their head.

They slapped him as they sunbathed
they slapped him in their hair,
they slapped him on their noses
they slapped him everywhere.

They flapped at him with papers
they swished at him with sticks,
and sprayed at him with poison
 - and other nasty tricks.

No -

No-one much liked Bertie
he led a rotten life -
until
one day whilst buzzing
he found himself a wife!

He found himself a pretty maid
big eyes and coat of blue,
They have ten thousand children
and teach them tricks to do.
They teach them how to dance on chips,
to tickle
    buzzzz
         and fly...
crawl around on people
and crawl around on pies.

36

They teach them upside walking
downside walking too,
climbing on the windows
and swimming in the stew.

Bertie is so happy now
and I'm sure you're glad to know
he's changed his name from Bertie Fly.
He's now called Mr. Blow.

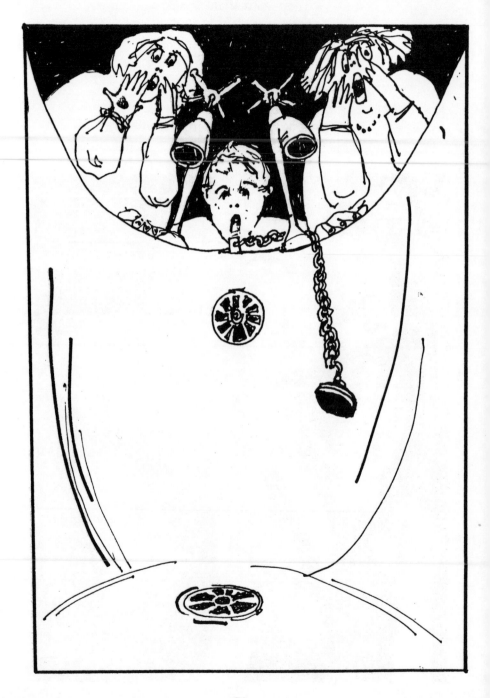

SPIDER IN THE BATH

Being stuck - inside a barf
is not really - called a larf.
Climbing holes with walls like ice
is not fun
and is not nice.
Even folk with spider's skill
slip and s
       l
        i
         d
          e
            upon this hill.

People come
and look
then scream -
turn on taps that hissssss
and steam.
Rivers spurt
and pools appear
spider folk get filled with fear...
Then whirlpools start
and gurgles come,
it isn't what you call - much fun.
We try to climb the walls again
but showers of spray begin to rain.
              We slip
              we fall
              our legs won't grip -

So pick us out we never nip.
We'll be your friends for evermore
if you will put us on the floor.
We'll run
We'll hide
a mile away -

       And bath with you,
         another day.

40

DEAD CAT

There's a dead cat in the roadway,
I heard the children tell.
It wears a russet collar
And it wears a silver bell.
It wears a shroud of tortoiseshell
With a pattern fine as lace
And it's lying in the gutter
With a smile upon it's face.
There's a dead cat in the gutter
And it's outside number four,
Eyes as white as lilies
And blood upon it's paw.
It dreams of bygone battles.
It dreams of cat-time fears,
And scratching playful children
And playful children's tears.
It dreams the stolen chicken,
The songbird slain at dawn,
And fires and feasts and fishes,
And bloodsteps on the lawn.
It smiles through ravaged thrush nests
And through the broken flowers,
And scratchings on the sofa
In the winter warmtime hours.
So, sleep your wicked catsmile,
Of secrets you can't tell.
And I'll lay you in the bushes
But, I'll keep your silver bell.

FRIDAY NIGHT

On Friday's

our dog

goes out

alone

- with a woggle on it's tail.

Ben says he goes to cubs.

Lord Nelson

W Shakespeare

Elizabeth I
Regina

Elizabeth II

Frank Burrows.

Elizabeth III

✝

43

ONE SPIT DEEP

One spit deep -
and a wedding gift teaspoon
untarnished by time
quicksilver winks from a muddied lair.
One spit deep -

> Ben's plastic pistol
> abandoned in the battle of The Birthday Party
> (1975)
> counts it's notches
> beside blue and white willow
> and the same old story.

'Happy Christmas Lily'
signals a dead gift token
- strangled by soggy tinsel
whilst long lost biros blink
                    recall light
and their last note to mother
                    father
                    lover
                    milkman
or GCSE Examination Board.

All is quiet one spit down.
Milk tops forget to rustle
and worms never cry.

All is quiet in Passchaendale
and all lost coins are pence.

WET PLAYTIME

Wayne has lost his slippers,
He left 'em on his chair,
Liza Wilson saw 'em -
At playtime they was there.

Martin Doughty touched 'em,
He threw them near the sink,
He threw them in the corner
'Cos he said they made a stink.

Debbie saw him do it
And the dinner lady knows.
She stood him in the corner,
Right next to Billy Rose.

The dinner lady's angry.
The playground lady's cross.
One's shouting in the lobby
And the other's caught Paul Ross.

Paul Ross - he had the slipper,
Tom James caused all the noise,
And they're standing by the staffroom
With thirty other boys.

Five have lost their sarnies,
Five have lost their coats,
Five have found some sarnies
And five have found five coats.

Five have lost the hamster,
Two know where it's hid,
And Emma's in the dustbin
And Sarah's thrown the lid.

It's another wet-time playtime,
A day of all 'being in'.
The game's called 'Catch the Culprit'
And the teachers never win!

BOGLINS 88

It is dry
It is warm
It is bright as gurkha knives
In Jack's Mini-market.
Tigered shells from alien seas
Wink in neon.
Circling postcards smile promises
                    of what tomorrow
                        the day after
                            or
                    the day after that
                        could be.

Suncreams -
Redcapped
And plump as piglets
Shoulder shelves
Whilst grinning ducks
Inflated with idiocy
Watch me buy my next tube
                    of Raincream.

The cardboard ladies smile.

THINGS I LIKED ABOUT SCHOOL

Wiping dinner tables,
Mixing up the paint.
The day we had the Assembly
And I saw an Infant faint.
The day we had a fire alarm,
The day the budgie died,

...

And chips
And crisps
And fizzy dips ...
And games like run and hide.
I loved the wet day playtimes -
When everybody stayed in
And everyone read comics
And made a great big din.

    I loved the window cleaners
    Who came at story time,
    - pulled faces at the teachers
    And made those funny signs.
    I loved the policeman coming
    The nurse who looked at hair,
    And folding all the tables
    And stacking all the chairs.

        I only disliked -
            lessons
        Like ... English, Maths and Craft
        And
        Worst of all was poetry.

        Poets must be daft.

GOODNIGHT TO MY BLACKBIRD

Goodnight, to my blackbird.
Goodnight, my black car,
I'm drawing my curtain
Goodnight, to my star.
Goodnight, to my cupboard
               my clock
               and my mat
my hamster is waking
and so is the cat.

My pillows are puffing,
the bed creaks
'Hello'.
Legs as strong as iron
but nowhere to go ...

Nowhere to travel,
Nowhere to run,
no secret islands
or pirates
or fun.

But I have my islands
my night will be bright.
My dreams are arriving,
So switch off my light.